WHEN I GROW UP

WHEN I GROW UP

written by

Elyse Sitner Barroway

illustrated by

Leire Ramos Castro

LUMINARE PRESS

WWW.LUMINAREPRESS.COM

Illustrations by Leire Ramos Castro
Graphic design by Claire Flint Last

Luminare Press
442 Charnelton St.
Eugene, OR 97401
www.luminarepress.com

LCCN: 2021908854
ISBN: 978-1-64388-656-5

To Jake and Jessie—the ones who made me
a mother, teacher, nurse, cheerleader, referee,
chauffeur, short-order cook, fashion consultant,
and finally a friend

Love, Mom

When I grow up,
I want to be a doctor.

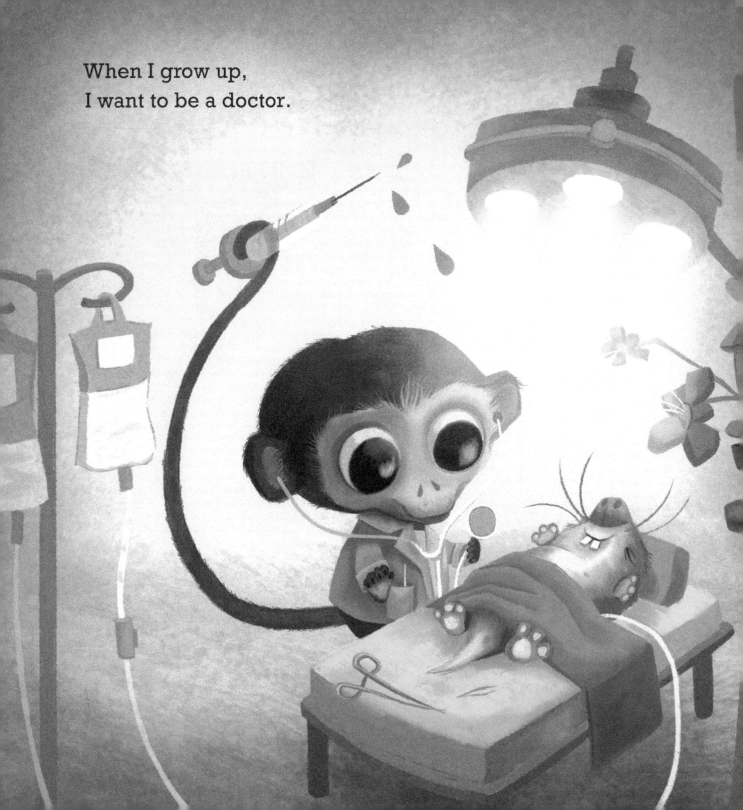

When you grow up,
I want you to be
compassionate.

When I grow up, I want to be a teacher.

When you grow up,
I want you to be kind.

When I grow up, I want to be a ballerina.

When you grow up,
I want you to be passionate.

When I grow up,
I want to be an astronaut.

When you grow up,
I want you to be courageous.

When I grow up,
I want to be a software developer.

When you grow up,
I want you to be reliable.

Follow your passions.

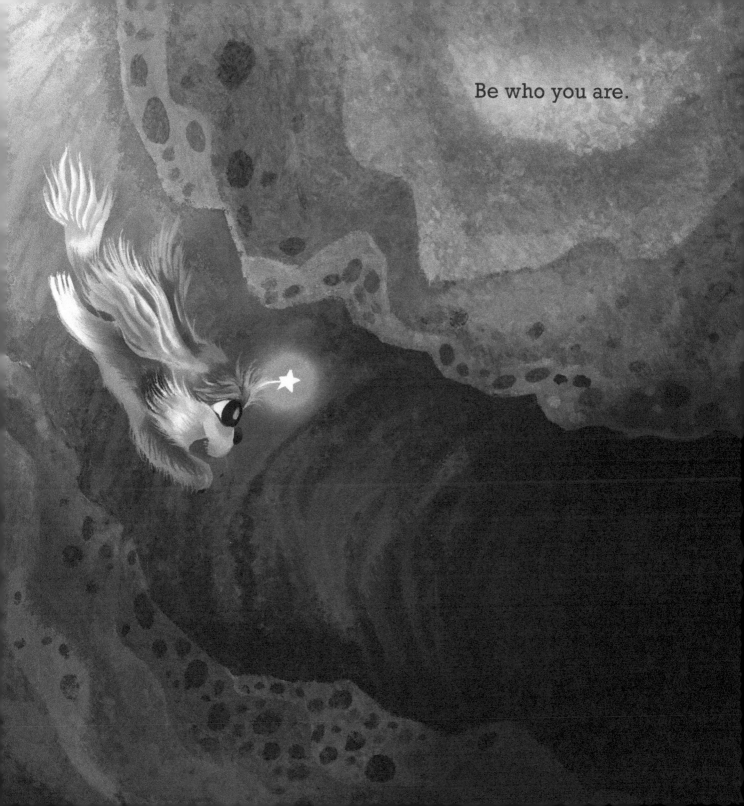

Be who you are.

You'll always shine bright.

You're always my star.

When I grow up,
I want to be an athlete.

When you grow up,
I want you to be confident.

When I grow up,
I want to be a police officer.

When you grow up, I want you to be empathetic.

When I grow up, I want to be an architect.

When you grow up,
I want you to be charitable.

When I grow up,
I want to be a movie star.

When you grow up,
I want you to be considerate.

When I grow up,
I want to be a chef.

When you grow up,
I want you to be adventurous.

Follow your passions.

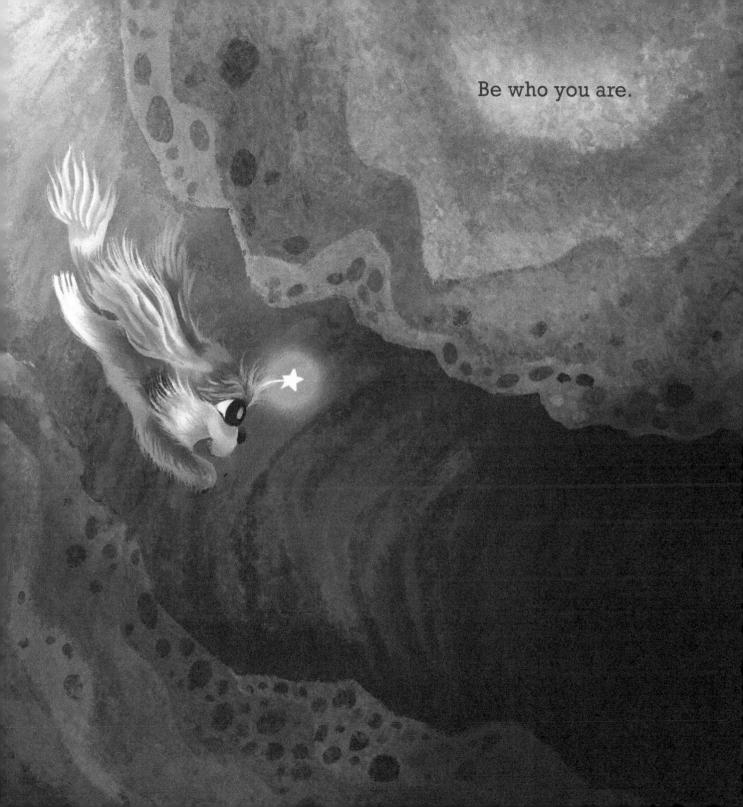

Be who you are.

You'll always shine bright.

You're always my star.

When I grow up,
I want to be a scientist.

When you grow up,
I want you to be happy.

When I grow up,
I want to be the president.

When you grow up, I want you to be you.

GLOSSARY

Adventurous:
willing to take risks or try new experiences

Charitable:
assisting those in need, generous

Compassionate:
showing concern for others

Confident:
believing in yourself
and your abilities

Considerate:
careful not to hurt others

Courageous:
brave

Empathetic:
showing an ability to understand
and share the feelings of others

Happy:
feeling pleasure

Kind:
having a friendly nature

Passionate:
showing strong feelings
or strong beliefs

Reliable:
able to be trusted

ABOUT THE AUTHOR

Elyse Sitner Barroway was born and raised outside of Philadelphia. She graduated from the Wharton School of the University of Pennsylvania with a bachelor of science degree in economics. She worked in finance and management training for eight years before leaving the corporate world to raise her two wonderful children.

The idea for this book came to her as she was packing up her son to move him home from his junior year of college. She realized that the "full-time job" of raising her kids was almost done, and she hoped that she had instilled the values that would make them good, productive members of society. So much focus is placed on what you do as a grown-up, but she wants to emphasize the importance of values, following your passions, and staying true to yourself.

She currently resides in Haverford, Pennsylvania, with her family and her beloved dog, Bandit.

For more info please visit
ElyseSitnerBarroway.com

ABOUT THE ILLUSTRATOR?

Leire Ramos Castro was born in San Sebastián, in the Basque Country, located in the north of Spain.

She graduated from Complutense University of Madrid with a degree in Art. She traveled for several years through different countries until settling in Lisbon, where she currently resides. The continuous contact with other cultures has allowed her to develop a good sense of creativity and adaptation.

She started her professional career as an illustrator eight years ago and her specialty is children's books. She is always looking for new challenges and interested in exploring professional opportunities and new artistic collaborations.

For more info please visit
www.LeireRamosCastro.com

CPSIA information can be obtained
at www.ICGtesting.com
Printed in the USA
LVHW071327150721
692789LV00002B/27

9 781643 886565